AF626058

Ursula Mamlok

Above Clouds

for viola and piano

2013/14

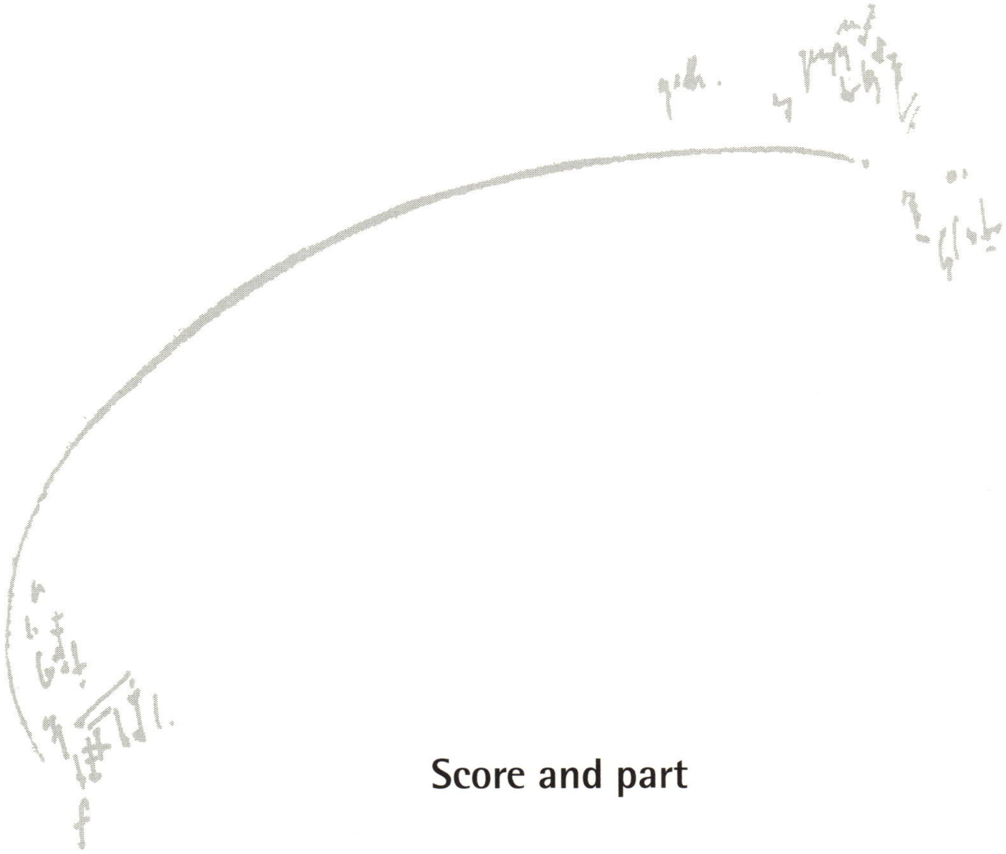

Score and part

BOOSEY & HAWKES
BOTE & BOCK

Dedicated to Stephanie Griffin and Cheryl Seltzer

Ursula Mamlok
Above Clouds
for viola and piano
(2013/14)

First Performance:	Center for Jewish History, New York City March 31, 2014 Stephanie Griffin (Viola) Cheryl Seltzer (Piano)
German Permiere:	Konzerthaus Berlin 21. November 2014 Hartmut Rohde (Viola) Holger Groschopp (Piano)
Duration:	9‘

www.boosey.com

AN IMAGEM COMPANY

BB 3410
ISMN 979-0-2025-3410-6
ISBN 978-3-7931-4107-5

Above Clouds
for viola and piano

I.

As in a dream
Wie im Traum

Ursula Mamlok
(2013/14)

 ISMN 979-0-2025-3410-6

II.

Scurrying
Huschend

♪ = 104

poco rit.
a tempo
arco
pizz.
pizz.
cantabile
dim.
cresc.
cresc.
sub.

cantabile
pizz.
p cresc.
sub. p
mp
mp cantabile
cresc.
(pizz.)
arco
p
pp
bring out E♮
e''' hervorheben
mf
f
f sub.
fff
sfz
cresc.
mp
rit.
a tempo
arco
pizz.
pp misterioso
pp
misterioso

*) Dampen struck note inside piano.
Saite im Innern des Flügels abdämpfen.

III.

Calm and tender
Ruhig und zart

♩ = ca. 52

*) Dampen struck note inside piano.
Saite im Innern des Flügels abdämpfen.

Ursula Mamlok

Above Clouds

for viola and piano

2013/14

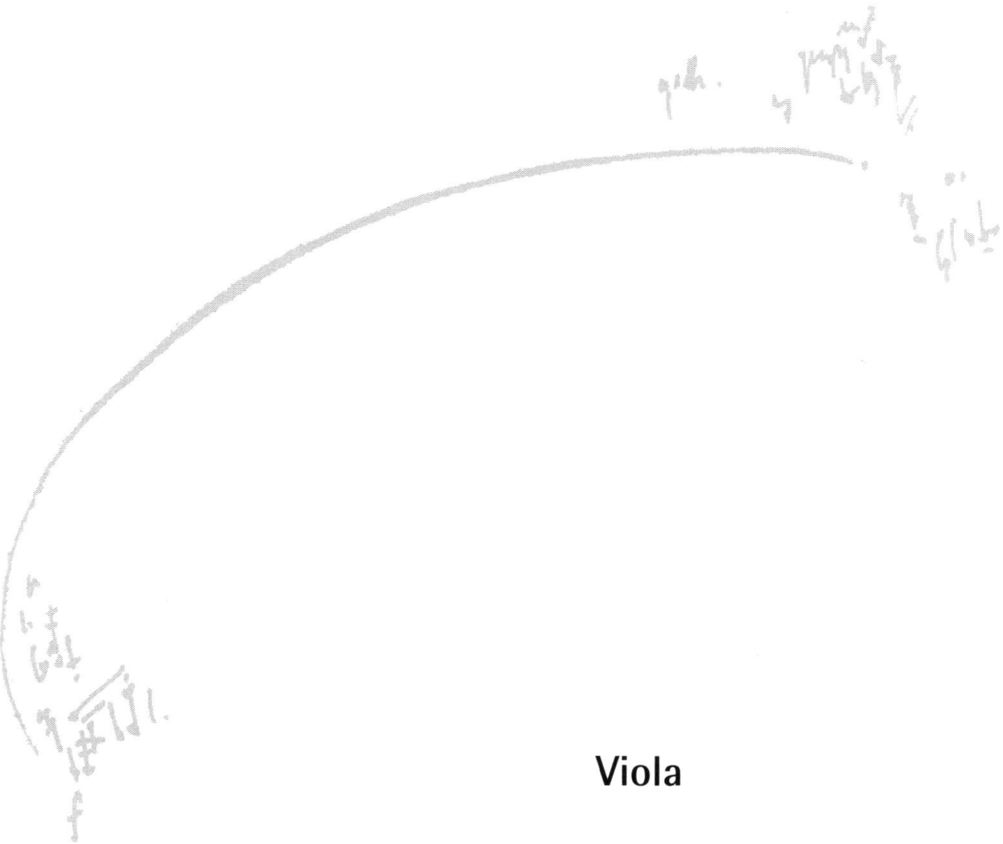

Viola

BOOSEY & HAWKES
BOTE & BOCK

Dedicated to Stephanie Griffin and Cheryl Seltzer

Ursula Mamlok
Above Clouds
for viola and piano
(2013/14)

First Performance:	Center for Jewish History, New York City March 31, 2014 Stephanie Griffin (Viola) Cheryl Seltzer (Piano)
German Permiere:	Konzerthaus Berlin 21. November 2014 Hartmut Rohde (Viola) Holger Groschopp (Piano)
Duration:	9‘

www.boosey.com

AN IMAGEM COMPANY

BB 3410
ISMN 979-0-2025-3410-6
ISBN 978-3-7931-4107-5

Above Clouds

for viola and piano

I.

Ursula Mamlok
(2013/14)

As in a dream
Wie im Traum
♩ = ca. 54

 ISMN 979-0-2025-3410-6

II.

Scurrying
Huschend
♪ = 104

15
19
21
25
cantabile
pizz.
mp cantabile
29
(pizz.)
arco
p cresc.
sub. p
pp sub.
f sub.

*) Dampen struck note inside piano.
Saite im Innern des Flügels abdämpfen.

Page blank for page turn

Blankoseite für günstige Wendestellen

III.

Calm and tender

Ruhig und zart

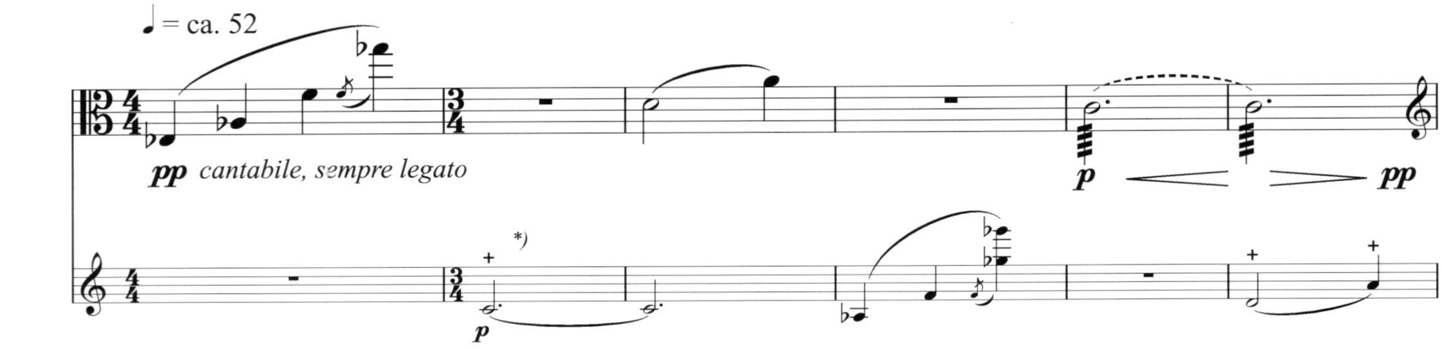

**) Dampen struck note inside piano.*
Saite im Innern des Flügels abdämpfen.

arco
sub.
espr.
dim.
non trem.

IV.

Capriccioso (♩. = 84)

20
molto rit.
dim.
25
♩ = 54
molto cantabile
scherzando
p dolce
pp scherzando
30
mp dim.
35
Tempo I ♩. = 84
Tempo II ♩ = 54
pizz.
dim.

40
arco
Tempo I ♩. = 84
48
54
cresc.
dim.
Slow
(Tempo II ♩ = 54)
sub.
60
Tempo I ♩. = 84
cresc.
dim.
65
molto rit.
pizz.

23
arco
p
pp
p
f
p
p
p
pp
f
sub. ff
29
mp
p
mf
p
mp
p
pp
p
mf
p
pp
mp
mf
34
mp
pp
f
mf
espr.
mf
mf
f
mf
39
non trem.
p
dim.
pp
pp

IV.

Capriccioso (♩. = 84)

molto rit.
20
dim.
25
♩ = 54
molto cantabile
scherzando
molto cantabile
p dolce
pp scherzando
30
dim.
35
Tempo I ♩. = 84
Tempo II ♩ = 54
pizz.
arco
dim.

Tempo I ♩. = 84
41
48
dim.
54
cresc.
Slow
(Tempo II ♩ = 54)
sub.

Tempo I ♩. = 84
60
mp cresc. f
mp cresc. f
ff
dim.
dim.
molto rit.
65
pizz.
p pp
pp
p